ACHIEVE ★
The Tricky Bits
English
Practice Questions

RISING ★ STARS

Rising Stars UK Ltd., 22 Grafton Street, London W1S 4EX

www.risingstars-uk.com

All facts are correct at time of going to press.

First published 2008
This edition 2010

Text, design and layout © 2008 Rising Stars UK Ltd.

Written by: Sam French
Series editor: Richard Cooper
Illustrations: Phill Burrows; J B Illustrations; Tony Randell
Design: Neil Hawkins
Cover design: Burville-Riley Partnership

Rising Stars are grateful to the QCA for permission to reproduce the following Key Stage 2 past test questions:
p29 Short writing 2003: A New Toy; p31 Short writing 2006: Endangered Creature; p34 Long writing 2005: Can I Stay Up?; p35 Long writing 2001: Tried and Tested; p38 Long writing 2006: Dear Diary; p39 Long writing 2003: The Queue.

The publishers and author would also like to thank the following for permission to use copyright material:
p10 *Applemoon* © Rose Flint, reproduced by kind permission of Rose Flint; p20 Extract from *Kensuke's Kingdom* by Michael Morpurgo, Egmont Books.

British Library Cataloguing in Publication Data
A CIP record for this book is available from the British Library.

ISBN 978-1-84680-655-1

Printed by Craft Print International Ltd, Singapore

Contents

The answers can be found in a pull-out section in the middle of this book.

Use of language, rhyme and rhythm

The Jabberwocky

`Twas brillig, and the slithy toves
    Did gyre and gimble in the wabe:
 All mimsy were the borogoves,
    And the mome raths outgrabe.

"Beware the Jabberwock, my son!
    The jaws that bite, the claws that catch!
Beware the Jubjub bird, and shun
    The frumious Bandersnatch!"

He took his vorpal sword in hand:
    Long time the manxome foe he sought --
So rested he by the Tumtum tree,
    And stood awhile in thought.

And, as in uffish thought he stood,
    The Jabberwock, with eyes of flame,
Came whiffling through the tulgey wood,
    And burbled as it came!

One, two! One, two! And through and through
    The vorpal blade went snicker-snack!
He left it dead, and with its head
    He went galumphing back.

"And, has thou slain the Jabberwock?
    Come to my arms, my beamish boy!
O frabjous day! Callooh! Callay!'
    He chortled in his joy.

`Twas brillig, and the slithy toves
    Did gyre and gimble in the wabe;
All mimsy were the borogoves,
    And the mome raths outgrabe.

Lewis Carroll

1 Why is this poem difficult to understand initially?

_____

1 mark · 1

2 What do you think the following words could mean?

a) *gyre and gimble*

_____

1 mark · 2a

b) *brillig*

_____

1 mark · 2b

c) *O frabjous day! Callooh! Callay!*

_____

_____

1 mark · 2c

3 We don't know what *vorpal* means, but why does its addition help us picture the boy's sword?

_____

2 marks · 3

4 **a)** What is the rhyming pattern in the poem?

_____

2 marks · 4a

b) How does the rhyming help us read the poem?

_____

1 mark · 4b

5 What are the advantages for the poet and the reader in using made-up words? Consider:
• rhyming;
• meaning of the poem;
• enjoyment of the poem for the reader.

_____

_____

_____

_____

_____

_____

3 marks · 5

6 Did you enjoy this poem? Use examples from the poem to justify your thoughts. Use a separate sheet of paper to write your answer.

3 marks · 6

Total marks for this topic

Stylistic choices

The Pied Piper of Hamelin

This is an extract of a long narrative poem about the people of the town of Hamelin in Germany, who were overrun by rats and saved by a mysterious man playing a musical pipe.

Hamelin Town's in Brunswick,
By famous Hanover city;
The river Weser, deep and wide,
Washes its wall on the southern side;
A pleasanter spot you never spied;
But, when begins my ditty,
Almost five hundred years ago,
To see the townsfolk suffer so
From vermin, was a pity.

Rats!
They fought the dogs and killed the cats,
And bit the babies in the cradles,
And ate the cheeses out of the vats,
And licked the soup from the cooks' own ladles,
Split open the kegs of salted sprats,
Made nests inside men's Sunday hats,
And even spoiled the women's chats,
By drowning their speaking
With shrieking and squeaking
In fifty different sharps and flats.

Great rats, small rats, lean rats, brawny rats,
Brown rats, black rats, grey rats, tawny rats,
Grave old plodders, gay young friskers,
Fathers, mothers, uncles, cousins,
Cocking tails and pricking whiskers,
Families by tens and dozens,
Brothers, sisters, husbands, wives --
Followed the Piper for their lives.
From street to street he piped advancing,
And step for step they followed dancing,
Until they came to the river Weser
Wherein all plunged and perished!

Robert Browning

1 How can you tell that the poet thought the town of Brunswick was a good place at the beginning of the poem?

_____

_____

1 mark

2 How does the first line of the second verse differ to the others and why is it effective?

_____

1 mark

3 Use the second verse to find out four ways the rats were causing havoc in Hamelin.

_____

_____

_____

_____

2 marks

4 The first seven lines of the third verse all describe the rats. Why do you think the poet uses so much description?

_____

_____

2 marks

5 This poem was published in 1842. Find three examples of language choices that tell you this is not a modern poem.

_____

_____

_____

3 marks

6 How does this poem make you feel? What techniques does the poet use to create that effect?

_____

_____

_____

3 marks

7 Do you think this poem is fact, fiction or a mix of both? Justify your answer with examples from the poem.

_____

_____

_____

3 marks

Total marks for this topic

Figurative language

The Highwayman

The wind was a torrent of darkness among the
    gusty trees,
The moon was a ghostly galleon tossed upon
    cloudy seas,
The road was a ribbon of moonlight, over the
    purple moor,
And the highwayman came riding--
Riding--riding--
The highwayman came riding, up to the old inn-door.

He'd a French cocked-hat on his forehead, a bunch of lace
    at his chin,
A coat of the claret velvet, and breeches of brown doe-skin;
They fitted with never a wrinkle: his boots were up to the
    thigh!
And he rode with a jewelled twinkle,
His pistol butts a-twinkle,
His rapier hilt a-twinkle, under the jewelled sky.

Over the cobbles he clattered and clashed in the dark inn-yard,
And he tapped with his whip on the shutters, but all was locked and barred;
He whistled a tune to the window, and who should be waiting there
But the landlord's black-eyed daughter,
Bess, the landlord's daughter,
Plaiting a dark red love-knot into her long black hair.

And dark in the old inn-yard a stable-wicket creaked
Where Tim the ostler listened; his face was white and peaked;
His eyes were hollows of madness, his hair like mouldy hay,
But he loved the landlord's daughter,
The landlord's red-lipped daughter,
Dumb as a dog he listened, and he heard the robber say:

"One kiss, my bonny sweetheart, I'm after a prize to-night,
But I shall be back with the yellow gold before the morning light;
Yet, if they press me sharply, and harry me through the day,
Then look for me by moonlight,
Watch for me by moonlight,
I'll come to thee by moonlight, though hell should bar the way."

He rose upright in the stirrups; he scarce could reach her hand,
But she loosened her hair i' the casement! His face burnt like a brand
As the black cascade of perfume came tumbling over his breast;
And he kissed its waves in the moonlight,
(Oh, sweet black waves in the moonlight!)
Then he tugged at his rein in the moonlight, and galloped away to the West.

Alfred Noyes

1 **a)** How do the first three lines of the poem help to create the atmosphere of the poem?

_____

_____

1a
2 marks

b) *And the highwayman came riding--*
Riding--riding--
The highwayman came riding, up to the old inn-door.

What impact does this repetition have on the reader?

_____

_____

1b
1 mark

2 The poet describes the highwayman's clothes very clearly. What does this description tell you about the character?

_____

_____

2
2 marks

3 Describe Tim the ostler in your own words. What sort of person do you think he is? Use evidence from the poem to support your view.

_____

_____

_____

3
3 marks

4 The highwayman is basically a thief, someone who stops rich people at gun point and steals their jewels and money – but Bess loved him. Imagine you are Bess. Justify why you are in love with a criminal.

_____

_____

_____

_____

4
3 marks

5 *Over the <u>cobbles</u> he <u>clattered</u> and <u>clashed</u> in the dark inn-yard.*

Think of two reasons why the author's choices of words are particularly effective.

_____

_____

_____

5
2 marks

Total marks for this topic

Word choices and impact – authorial intent

Applemoon

Something woke me: startle-sound
or moonlight. The house dreamt
like an old cat, but I
looked out my window.

And night was day in a midnight
moon-flood. Mazy moon
flaring a halo of quick clouds
running the big black sky.
And I saw a thousand windfall apples
lying luminous as sea-stone beached
below the spiky silver trees.

So, shivering I
mouse-went out
with a basket, barefoot, toes
curling in the cold;
and singing soft
took ripe reluctant apples
under close and curious stars.

Only soon I saw
my shadow was not
the same as I;
it stooped more-
had its own thinness ...
and our fingers
never met.

I quick-ran back
the house so
sleepy-warm, sure.
But looking out through curtain lace
I saw my shadow linger
moving slow and crooked, plucking
shadow apples
from the shining moony grass.

Rose Flint

(1) What does *The house dreamt like an old cat* mean?
How does this contrast with the poet's feelings?

_____

_____

_____

2 marks

(2) Describe what the poet could see from her window.

_____

_____

_____

2 marks

3 **a)** Find three examples of alliteration in the poem.

_____

_____

_____

3a
1 mark

b) Why do you think the poet used alliteration here?

_____

_____

_____

3b
3 marks

4 What has happened to the poet's shadow and why?

_____

_____

_____

_____

4
3 marks

5 **a)** Find three examples where the poet links words with a hypen.

_____

_____

_____

5a
1 mark

b) Why do you think she does this?

_____

_____

_____

5b
2 marks

6 How does the poem make you feel? Explain how the poet chooses particular words and phrases to create the atmosphere of the poem.

_____

_____

_____

_____

_____

6
3 marks

Total marks for this topic

Fiction

I, Coriander

A Tale to Tell

It is night, and our old house by the river is finally quiet. The baby has stopped its crying and been soothed back to sleep. Only the gentle lapping of the Thames can be heard outside my window. London is wrapped in a deep sleep, waiting for the watchman to call in the new day.

I have lit the first of seven candles to write my story by. On the table next to me is the silk purse that holds my mother's pearls and beside it is the ebony casket whose treasure I am only now beginning to understand. Next to that, shining nearly as bright as the moon, stands a pair of silver shoes.

I have a great many more things to tell, of how I came by the silver shoes and more. And this being my story and a fairy tale besides, I will start once upon a time …

My name is Coriander Hobie. I am the only child of Thomas and Eleanor Hobie, being born in this house in the year of Our Lord 1643. It is just a stone's throw from London Bridge, with the river running past the windows at the back. To the front is my mother's once beautiful walled garden that leads through a wooden door out on to the bustling city street.

Sally Gardner

1 How does the description used in the first paragraph help us create a really clear picture of the setting of this story? Use examples of words or phrases used by the author to explain your reasoning and explain if you would like to live there.

_____

_____

_____

3 marks | 1

2 **a)** Is the front garden beautiful now? How can you tell?

_____

_____

1 mark | 2a

b) What might the garden be like now?

_____

_____

1 mark | 2b

3 The narrator of this story is writing by candlelight. Why would this be necessary?

_____

1 mark | 3

4 How old do you think the narrator is?

_____

1 mark | 4

5 Her mother used to have a beautiful garden and she named her daughter after the herb coriander. What does this tell us about the mother?

_____

_____

1 mark | 5

6 Why do you think Coriander's mother is no longer looking after the garden? What has happened to her? Use clues from the story to explain your answer.

_____

_____

_____

_____

2 marks | 6

Total marks for this topic

13

Non-fiction writing

The following are extracts from interviews with children who live in villages who have benefited from help from a charity called WaterAid. WaterAid's mission is to overcome poverty by enabling the world's poorest people to gain access to safe water, sanitation and hygiene education.

Solomon's story

Solomon is 11 years old and lives in Ogwete village in Uganda. WaterAid and a local organisation helped the village community to build a borehole (well) so everyone had access to clean, safe drinking water.

The community have plans to build another well so people don't have to walk so far for water.

Hi Solomon, how did you collect water before the borehole was built?
"My family used to collect water from the swamp and the water was milky and smelt very bad. Now that we have a borehole in the village we use it to collect drinking water. The water looks clean now and it doesn't make us ill. We still use the swamp water for washing utensils and sometimes for bathing because the borehole is half an hour away."

How has having a clean and safe supply of water affected your life?
"My family have also built a dish rack, a bathing shelter and a latrine. I'm very proud of my village and my home now.

I like the new bathing shelter because it is much more private. The shelter is made from trees which we collected from around our home."

What have you learnt about how to keep healthy?
"I know that I should wash my hands after using the latrine so that I do not get ill. It gives you a stomach ache if you have dirty hands and then eat food."

Vasanthi's story

Vasanthi lives in the southern state of Tamil Nadu, India. She is 10 years old and goes to Marachipatti Primary School.

The school worked with WaterAid to build clean toilets and train people to talk about how to prevent disease.

Before the new toilets were built, children were often ill. Now Vasanthi and her classmates chat about health with their parents so the whole community learn how to have healthier lives.

Hello Vasanthi, can you tell me what difference the toilet block has made to your life at school?
"Before we had the toilets we had to use the thorn bushes on the outskirts of the village. Sometimes snakes would come and disturb us. I would run away as quickly as possible. This wasn't much fun."

Your school has a health club – what did you learn from it?
"Through the personal hygiene committee, we have learnt to cut our nails and wear clean clothes."

What information do you give to others about personal hygiene?
"If somebody else comes to school looking dirty we ask their parents to send them cleaner next time. We also tell our parents to wash their hair, clean their teeth and wash their hands with soap after handling garbage."

Vasanthi and her classmates queue to use the toilets.

1 What sorts of things might be in the water from the swamp that Solomon had to use?

_____

1 mark

2 The local villagers are clearly enthusiastic about their new borehole. How can you tell?

_____

_____

1 mark

3 How have the new toilets improved life for Vasanthi?

_____

_____

2 marks

4 Why do you think Vasanthi and her friends are teaching the adults, rather than the other way round?

_____

_____

_____

3 marks

5 What do Solomon and Vasanthi have in common and how are they different?

_____

_____

_____

_____

3 marks

6 Do you think WaterAid is a worthwhile charity? Why? Use evidence from both interviews to support your answer.

_____

_____

_____

_____

3 marks

7 How could you help WaterAid help more people?

_____

1 mark

Total marks for this topic

15

Using dialogue to infer character

These questions are about the opening paragraphs to the classic adventure story *Treasure Island* by Robert Louis Stevenson.

The story was written over 100 years ago but it still remains popular today and was adapted for the film *Treasure Planet*.

Some of the language needs to be read quite carefully and it helps if you can picture the scene.

The person talking at the beginning of the story is the hero of the tale – a boy called Jim Hawkins. He is remembering how his adventures began when a mysterious character turned up at his parents' inn, 'The Admiral Benbow', looking for a place to stay.

Part One – The Old Buccaneer

Chapter 1: The Old Sea-dog at the Admiral Benbow

Squire Trelawney, Dr. Livesey, and the rest of these gentlemen having asked me to write down the whole particulars about Treasure Island, from the beginning to the end, keeping nothing back but the bearings of the island, and that only because there is still treasure not yet lifted, I take up my pen in the year of grace 1700 and go back to the time when my father kept the Admiral Benbow inn and the brown old seaman with the sabre cut first took up his lodging under our roof.

I remember him as if it were yesterday, as he came plodding to the inn door, his sea-chest following behind him in a hand-barrow – a tall, strong, heavy, nut-brown man, his tarry pigtail falling over the shoulder of his soiled blue coat, his hands ragged and scarred, with black, broken nails, and the sabre cut across one cheek, a dirty, livid white. I remember him looking round the cove and whistling to himself as he did so, and then breaking out in that old sea-song that he sang so often afterwards:

"Fifteen men on the dead man's chest –

Yo-ho-ho, and a bottle of rum!"

in the high, old tottering voice that seemed to have been tuned and broken at the capstan bars. Then he rapped on the door with a bit of stick like a handspike that he carried, and when my father appeared, called roughly for a glass of rum. This, when it was brought to him, he drank slowly, like a connoisseur, lingering on the taste and still looking about him at the cliffs and up at our signboard.

"This is a handy cove," says he at length; "and a pleasant sittyated grog-shop. Much company, mate?"

My father told him no, very little company, the more was the pity.

"Well, then," said he, "this is the berth for me. Here you, matey," he cried to the man who trundled the barrow; "bring up alongside and help up my chest. I'll stay here a bit," he continued. "I'm a plain man; rum and bacon and eggs is what I want, and that head up there for to watch ships off. What you mought call me? You mought call me captain. Oh, I see what you're at – there"; and he threw down three or four gold pieces on the threshold. "You can tell me when I've worked through that," says he, looking as fierce as a commander.

1 The visitor to the inn walks up singing and whistling. What clues does that give you about this character?

_____

_____

1 mark

2 This is an old story. What would be a modern way of saying _a pleasant sittyated grog-shop_?

_____

1 mark

3 Look for an extract in the text which shows that Jim has clear memories of the buccaneer's visit, even though it happened a long time ago.

_____

_____

1 mark

4 The visitor to the Admiral Benbow has a sabre cut on his face, scarred hands, a dirty coat, black nails and nut-brown skin. What does this tell us about his life at sea?

_____

_____

_____

1 mark

5 Why do you think Jim's dad said _no, very little company, more was the pity_?

_____

_____

1 mark

6 The visitor to the Admiral Benbow has a long speech at the end of the piece of text. From what he says, why do you think he chooses to stay at this particular inn?

_____

_____

_____

1 mark

Total marks for this topic

17

Using description to infer setting

Wind in the Willows

It is a cold winters evening and Mole and Ratty have paid an unexpected call on their friend Mr Badger.

He [Badger] shuffled on in front of them, carrying the light, and they followed him, nudging each other in an anticipating sort of way, down a long, gloomy, and, to tell the truth, decidedly shabby passage, into a sort of a central hall; out of which they could dimly see other long tunnel-like passages branching, passages mysterious and without apparent end. But there were doors in the hall as well– stout oaken comfortable-looking doors. One of these the Badger flung open, and at once they found themselves in all the glow and warmth of a large fire-lit kitchen.

The floor was well-worn red brick, and on the wide hearth burnt a fire of logs, between two attractive chimney-corners tucked away in the wall, well out of any suspicion of draught. A couple of high backed settles, facing each other on either side of the fire, gave further sitting accommodation for the sociably disposed. In the middle of the room stood a long table of plain boards placed on trestles, with benches down each side. At one end of it, where an arm-chair stood pushed back, were spread the remains of Badger's plain but ample supper. Rows of spotless plates winked from the shelves of the dresser at the far end of the room, and from the rafters overhead hung hams, bundles of dried herbs, nets of onions, and baskets of eggs. It seemed a place where … two or three friends of simple tastes could sit about as they pleased and eat and smoke and talk in comfort and contentment.

Kenneth Grahame

1 What were Mole and Ratty's thoughts about Badger's house? Why did they think this?

_____

_____

2 marks

2 How does the kitchen contrast to the passageways?

_____

_____

1 mark

3 What clues are there in the text that suggest Badger might enjoy cooking and entertaining?

_____

_____

_____

2 marks

4 Find the extract in the text that shows that Ratty and Mole were expecting to enjoy their evening with Badger.

_____

_____

_____

1 mark

5 This passage describes two parts of Badger's home – the cold, dirty and shabby passageways, and welcoming and comfortable kitchen. What do you think his bedroom would be like? Describe it and justify your answer.

_____

_____

_____

_____

_____

_____

3 marks

Total marks for this topic

Fiction

Kensuke's Kingdom

I disappeared on the night before my twelfth birthday. July 28, 1988. Only now can I at last tell the whole extraordinary story, the true story. Kensuke made me promise that I would say nothing, nothing at all, until at least ten years had passed. It was almost the last thing he said to me. I promised, and because of that I have had to live out a lie. I could let sleeping lies sleep on, but more than ten years have passed now. I have done school, done college, and had time to think. I owe it to my family and to my friends, all of whom I have deceived for so long, to tell the truth about my long disappearance, about how I lived to come back from the dead.

But there is another reason for speaking out now, a far, far better reason. Kensuke was a great man, a good man, and he was my friend. I want the world to know him as I knew him.

Until I was nearly eleven, until the letter came, life was just normal. There were the four of us in the house: my mother, my father, me, and Stella – Stella Artois, that is, my one-ear-up and one-ear-down black and white sheepdog, who always seemed to know what was about to happen before it did. But even she could not have forseen how that letter was going to change our lives forever.

Michael Morpurgo

1 What do you think was in the letter and what impact did it have on the lives of the family?

_____

1 mark

2 Who is narrating this tale?

_____

1 mark

3 How is the content of the first two paragraphs different to the third?

_____

_____

2 marks

4 Why is the first sentence of the book an excellent way to start a story?

_____

_____

1 mark

5 Who do you think Kensuke is and how is he involved in the narrator's story? What sort of person was he?

_____

_____

_____

3 marks

6 Why do you think the narrator of the story took his promise to Kensuke so seriously and didn't tell his story for 10 years?

_____

_____

2 marks

7 _I want the world to know him as I knew him._

What does this tell us about public opinion of Kensuke up until now?

_____

_____

2 marks

8 Can you make a prediction as to where the narrator was during his long disappearance and how he came back from the dead?

_____

_____

2 marks

Total marks for this topic

Non-fiction writing

The following fact boxes contain information about the life of Nelson Mandela. He is the world's most famous South African. He led the struggle for equal rights for blacks and whites in South Africa in the twentieth century.

The early years

Rolihlahla Mandela was born on 18th July 1918 in a rural part of South Africa. His grandfather had been a tribal King so he was born into an important family. He lived with his mum, dad and 12 brothers and sisters on a farm where they grew crops and kept cattle – but they didn't own the farm – it was owned by a white land owner who had to be paid with crops and meat. Black children in rural South Africa generally didn't go to school, but Mandela was lucky and was the first person from his family to ever go to school and he started in 1925. His white teacher changed his name to Nelson.

Political career

In 1940, Mandela arrived in the big city of Johannesburg without a job, home or any money. At this time, black people were not allowed the same rights as white people. This system was called apartheid. In this system, black people had to carry identity cards, were not allowed to travel, were not allowed to use "whites only" areas, like swimming pools and ice cream parlours. There were separate schools for blacks and whites too. The new friends he made in the city were politically active and they spent a lot of time discussing how badly treated black people were. They decided to do something about it. From 1948, onwards, Mandela dedicated his life to the struggle against apartheid and organised mass protests against these unjust laws. He was arrested and put in prison for the next 27 years.

Robben Island

Mandela and six of his comrades were sent to prison on Robben Island where they were met by armed guards with dogs. Robben Island is 8 miles off the coast of Africa. It was a high security prison where escape was impossible due to the strong sea currents and the sharks between the prison and the mainland. Life on Robben Island was brutal – the prisoners were fed badly, had to work all day breaking up rocks and were poorly clothed. They were rarely allowed visitors and had to live in solitary confinement. Despite these harsh conditions, the inmates managed to communicate with each other without the guards knowing and planned their lives once they were free.

Freedom

In 1990, Mandela was freed from prison and South Africa was changing. The world put pressure on the country to stop apartheid and in 1994 blacks were allowed to vote for the first time. At this time, Mandela won the Nobel Peace Prize for all his work to bring equality back to South Africa. Mandela was voted the first black president of South Africa and began to rebuild the country. He made sure that both black and white people had a say in how the country was run. He was a popular leader for many years. He retired from public life in 2004 when he was 86 and now lives quietly in the small village he was brought up in.

ANSWERS

READING COMPREHENSION

Page 5 – Use of language, rhyme and rhythm
1 It has lots of made up words in it.
2 As these words are nonsense, you can interpret them in any way you see fit but here are some examples.
  a) Verbs to describe movement of the Jabberwock – prowling.   **b)** Sounds a bit like brilliant – suggesting an amazing creature sneaking around.   **c)** Wow – it's amazing, well done – fantastic.
3 It makes it sound special. (*1 mark*) Perhaps a big sword to be used on special missions. (*1 mark*)
4 **a)** Lines 1 and 3 rhyme and lines 2 and 4 rhyme.   **b)** It helps the poem flow.
5 He doesn't have to be restrained by known words that rhyme, but can make up words that sound good and then make them rhyme. You can also create your own impression of the Jabberwock – made up words allow you to use your imagination more – this helps you enjoy the poem more.
6 Yes or no answers are both fine as long as they are justified with examples from poem.
  1 mark (gives an opinion acknowledging the nonsense words).
  2 marks (gives an opinion and mentions specific words used in the poem).
  3 marks (gives an opinion referring to parts of the poem with explanation).

Page 7 – Stylistic choices
1 *A pleasanter spot you never spied*
2 A one word line creates a big impact, and followed by an exclamation mark it adds emphasis.
3 Any four of: fought dogs; killed cats; bit babies; ate cheeses; licked soups; broke sprat kegs; made nests in hats; interrupted chats (*1 mark for two or three correct answers; 2 marks for all four correct*)
4 To explain how varied the rats were (*1 mark*) and to emphasise the numbers of rats in the town (*1 mark*).
5 *ditty, townsfolk, wherein*
6 It is a fast moving cheery poem, almost a song, as the poet calls it a ditty (*1 mark*). It is written as it would be spoken so it has a lively, interesting feeling to the story (*1 mark*). The rhyming patterns also help to lift the mood of the poem to create a fun and exciting poem (*1 mark*).
7 Probably a mix of both; there could be a town in Germany called Hamelin, near Brunswick and they could have had a rat problem so that part would be factual, but I think the part about the Pied Piper getting rid of the rats is fiction.

Page 9 – Figurative language
1 **a)** Use of metaphors to describe the weather conditions (*1 mark*), for example, *The moon was a ghostly galleon tossed upon cloudy seas* helps the reader create an image of a storm in their heads (*1 mark*).
  b) The poet repeats the word *riding* to show how long the highwayman was on his horse.
2 He was wealthy enough to afford the clothes and pistol jewels (*1 mark*), and he took a lot of trouble over his appearance (*1 mark*).
3 A man with pale skin, bad hair and big eyes sunk into his face (*1 mark*). He is not good looking and fashionable like the highwayman (*1 mark*). He is probably lonely as he works in the inn on his own. He might be jealous of the highwayman (*1 mark*).
4 Any three of: Bess loves the highwayman because he is handsome, rich and strong (*1 mark*); he brings her jewels that he gets from the rich people (*1 mark*); although Bess doesn't like him being a criminal, she still loves him (*1 mark*); also she lives on her own at the inn with Tim the Ostler, so she enjoys visits from the highwayman (*1 mark*).
5 They are examples of alliteration and onomatopoeia. Both techniques help the reader understand how loud the horses' hooves were on the stones of the courtyard.

Pages 10–11 – Word choices and impact – authorial intent
1 The simile is describing the house as settled, comfortable, contented, peaceful. The poet is alert, wakeful, could even be woken by moonlight.
2 Acceptable answers: clouds going quickly across the sky; bright moonlight flooding the garden; a lot of apples lying under spiky silver trees; trees in the moonlight. NB Sea-stones is incorrect. She cannot see them – the description is a simile.
3 **a)** Examples are 'singing soft', 'ripe reluctant', 'close and curious', 'curling in the cold'.
  b) Possible answers: to make the reader look at the description again/closely; to cluster the description/make it more powerful; create a balance within the verse.
4 The shadow detached from the poet and stayed in the garden after the poet went back upstairs. Possible answers: to experience the moonlight; to echo the apple picking; to show the poet doesn't really want to go back indoors.
5 **a)** startle-sound, moon-flood, mouse-went, sea-stone, quick-ran, sleepy-warm
  b) Possible answers: because it's unexpected and therefore effective; to make the reader look at the description again; to add rhythm/atmosphere to the poem; to create contrast within longer sentences.
6 It can make you feel whatever you like, but it is likely to be eerie or scary. You will need to quote words and phrases that exemplify your choices. You need to be able to think of two different examples to get two marks and then explain your views to get the third mark.

Page 13 – Inference and deduction – fiction
1 It tells us a lot about the setting, it uses different senses (*1 mark*) like the sound of the water lapping, and it uses a metaphor, *London is wrapped in a deep sleep* (*1 mark*). I would like to live there because it sounds like a peaceful and safe place to be (*1 mark*).
2 **a)** No, it says once *beautiful* garden, which means it isn't any more.   **b)** Overgrown with weeds and brambles and uncared for.
3 Because it is the 1600s and there was no electricity.
4 She is a young girl.

5 She liked plants and flowers.
6 She might have died and that is why Coriander has her pearls and ebony box and silver shoes.

Page 15 – Inference and deduction – non-fiction writing
1 Any one of: mud, insects, dirt, bacteria
2 They have made their own latrine, dish rack and bathing shelter.
3 Any two of: stopped her being ill which means she doesn't miss so much school (*1 mark*), so she is getting a better education (*1 mark*); she also avoids snakes (*1 mark*).
4 The children found out about hygiene from WaterAid. The adults wouldn't know about hygiene, as they were not used to having clean water.
5 Neither had a safe source of water and hygiene but have both been helped by WaterAid (*1 mark*). But Vasanthi has received help for herself and her whole school (*1 mark*); Solomon's help was for his village (*1 mark*).
6 **Yes**, WaterAid is a good charity because it provides clean water for people who have none (*1 mark*). It is a good charity because it works all over the world, like Africa and India (*1 mark*), and everyone should have the right to clean water, like Solomon and his family who are now able to wash (*1 mark*). **No**, it is not a worthwhile charity because if people like Vasanthi need clean water in their schools they should raise the funds themselves (*1 mark*); it is not a good use of money raised in Britain to send it all the way to India or Africa (*1 mark*). In Soloman's case, the borehole is half an hour away and that is too far (*1 mark*).
7 Raise money for them.

Page 17 – Using dialogue to infer character
1 He is either very happy or possibly drunk. He is singing a sea shanty sung by pirates, so maybe he is a pirate.
2 A pub in a pretty location.
3 *I remember him as if it were yesterday*
4 It was hard and he spent a lot of time outside as he has a suntan (*1 mark*). He does not spend much time looking after his appearance or cleaning his clothes (*1 mark*). He has had fights in the past as he has a scar on his face (*1 mark*).
5 Because he runs the inn and needs to make money from people staying.
6 Any three of: He likes the position of the inn (*1 mark*) and likes the fact that it doesn't have many visitors (*1 mark*). All he asks for is eggs, bacon and rum and a place to look out for ships from (*1 mark*). This suggests he is hiding from someone and wants to see them coming if they look for him at the inn (*1 mark*).

Page 19 – Using description to infer setting
1 They were unimpressed (*1 mark*), the passageways were long, gloomy and shabby (*1 mark*).
2 It is bright, clean and welcoming.
3 He had lots of seats around a long table (*1 mark*) and had lots of food hanging from the ceiling (*1 mark*).
4 *It seemed a place where … two or three friends of simple tastes could sit about as they pleased and eat and smoke and talk in comfort and contentment.*
5 He didn't waste money making the bits of his house he passes through nice and clean (*1 mark*) but likes to be comfortable (*1 mark*), so his bedroom would have a big bed with lots of pillows and a big fire to keep him warm (*1 mark*).

Page 21 – Justification of own opinion – fiction
1 Anything life changing e.g. moving home, emigration, lottery win, etc.
2 The child of the family.
3 The first two paragraphs are set in the present day and set the scene (*1 mark*), the third is in the past tense (*1 mark*).
4 Immediately it asks the reader questions and draws them into the plot. It is an exciting and unusual thing to happen as not many people disappear.
5 *1 mark (gives an opinion about his personality)*: I think Kensuke was someone involved in the disappearance of the narrator.
2 marks (gives an opinion and mentions specific words used in the story): Someone involved in his disappearance, but a good character during that time as the text says *a good man, and he was my friend*.
3 marks (gives an opinion referring to parts of the poem with explanation): I think Kensuke is a character that the narrator meets during the time he is missing – the character is misunderstood – the narrator likes him and thinks he is a good person, but other people disagree. I could tell that from lines the author wrote e.g. *a good man, and he was my friend and I want the world to know him as I knew him.*
6 Because Kensuke was such a good friend and the silence was so important to him.
7 He is not a popular character (*1 mark*), but the narrator wants to change that (*1 mark*).
8 Any reasonable answer e.g. shipwrecked on a desert island with Kensuke and then rescued by a boat.

Page 23 – Justification of own opinion – non-fiction writing
1 Because he needed a white name to be at school; it would help him fit in with the other white children.
2 **Yes**, because he lived with his family and had lots of brothers and sisters to play with and lived in the country so could play outside all day. **No**, because he had to work on the farm but give all the profits to the white land owners.
3 **Brave** – to take on the white oppression (*1 mark*) without any way to support himself and with risk of being imprisoned (*1 mark*). **Foolish** – to arrive in a city with nowhere to live (*1 mark*) no job and no home (*1 mark*). **Or** a mixture of both – *two points from one point of view and one from the other for all 3 marks.*
4 Really sad as he had lost his freedom, ability to talk to people who believed in the same things as him and was cut off from his family.
5 a) Any reasonable idea e.g. sign language, whispering when the guards weren't looking, talking at night from one cell to another.   b) They would probably talk about freedom and stopping apartheid.
6 **Yes**, probably because most white people would disagree with apartheid too (*1 mark*), and most people would rather live in a country that was fair (*1 mark*). **No**, some people, like the big land owners might not have liked him as his leadership meant they lost their land and power (*1 mark*). Some white people would have been happy with apartheid as it benefited them (*1 mark*). *Two points from one side and one from the other for all 3 marks.*

Page 25 – Justification of own opinion – poetry

1 In a countryside location (*1 mark*), it uses words *forest's ferny floor* and *leaf-fringed sill* (*1 mark*). It is in the middle of nowhere as it is really quiet (*1 mark*).

2 **a)** Possible answer: they are ghosts. **b)** They were murdered in the house.

3 No, the traveller was supposed to meet his friends there, but was late so missed the trouble that caused their deaths (*1 mark*) – the poet says '*Tell them I came … That I kept my word*' (*1 mark*).

4 Knocked

5 A historical poem because the traveller is travelling on horseback (*1 mark*) and the language is old fashioned e.g. *smote* and *Ay* (*1 mark*).

6 The next town because he is walking through a forest and in olden days, villages and towns were separated by forests. **Or** Home because he was asked to visit this house '*Tell them I came, and no one answered, That I kept my word,*' he said, so he will get back on his horse and return home.

7 *1 mark*: **Yes**, I enjoyed the poem because it uses interesting vocabulary that creates clear pictures in the reader's head. **No**, I did not enjoy the poem because it uses old fashioned language.

   2 marks: **Yes**, I enjoyed the poem because of its use of vocabulary and the feeling of mystery created; it raised lots of questions in my head about the traveller. **No**, I didn't like it because it uses complicated vocabulary and it doesn't tell us enough information about the traveller; I want my questions about the traveller answered.

   3 marks: **Yes**, I enjoyed the poem a lot because I liked the story it told and the sense of mystery that was created. I enjoyed the vocabulary choices, such as *Never the least stir made the listeners*; *Though every word he spake*; *Fell echoing through the shadowiness of the still house*; *From the one man left awake*. I liked the way the poet created a sense of mystery around the traveller and I was able to use my imagination to explain who he was and where he was going. **No**, I thought the poem was a bit dull, I didn't like the old fashioned way it was written as I like poems that are written in modern-day language. It would have helped me understand the poem more if I had known why the rest of the men were dead. I don't enjoy poems that are written about ghosts; I find them quite scary.

WRITING

Page 26 – Tale of courage

Paragraph 1 In a first person narrative, the setting will be described as seen by 'you'. Include the small details a child would notice. Put out some hooks for the reader by dropping hints of what is to come.

Paragraph 2 You should write about yourself in relation to others and track the effect the unfolding events have on you. The initial terror followed by the shame of being found out. This needs very powerful writing and would be a good place to use metaphor. Writing about what you imagine others to be thinking is another way to show the effect they are having on you. Include some dialogue to move the story on. Show the cruelty of others by their words and actions. Adjectives such as 'mocking' and 'scornful' could be used to describe the words and laughter. The imagined thoughts of others powerfully describe the effect of exposure on you.

Paragraph 3 Use a descriptive time connective to open the paragraph. Develop your character by writing about the dilemma you face. Enhance the description with physical aspects of fear. End with a cliffhanger.

Paragraph 4 This is an action paragraph and should be quite a contrast with the previous build up. Use short sentences and powerful verbs. Repetition may be a useful technique here. End the paragraph with relief and amazement.

Paragraph 5 Description given to explain how your unhappiness was resolved. Follow this with personal reflections. You need to show how you have been altered by the events. Reflect on the fact that you will never again have to worry about your fear being exposed.

Page 27 – A cautionary tale

Paragraph 1 This story starts with a crisis and must have a powerful first sentence. Effective action writing depends on the use of some short punchy sentences, powerful verbs and questions to make the reader wonder. Tension is created using techniques such as repetition or alliteration. This paragraph should develop the setting and begin to build up characters by their responses to the crisis.

Paragraph 2 This should be more than a retelling of previous events. It is a chance to develop the character through their reflection and feelings. Vary the sentence types you use. Plant a sentence that you are going to refer back to in your concluding remarks.

Paragraph 3 Use dialogue to develop characters and move the story forward. Show the relationship between characters by how they speak to each other and develop more than one viewpoint. Include information from all senses as the setting is described.

Paragraph 4 Use a descriptive time connective to move the story on to the rescue. You must create some tension when the success of the operation is in the balance – ellipsis would help create this. Do not aim to tell it all; leave the tale when help is arriving. Use powerful language – strong verbs, metaphors, short sentences for impact followed by longer ones to give more information.

Paragraph 5 Use another time connective phrase to move the story to safety, the consequences and reflections. Show how the experience has changed your character. End with a narrator's comment that ties in with an earlier part of the story.

Page 28 – A historical tale

Paragraph 1 You should use the first paragraph to establish your main character in the midst of a historical setting. Give your setting a name. Use the setting to say something about your character. Include sense impressions to develop the setting – what can the character see and hear? Add historical details as you describe incidents.

Paragraph 2 Use this paragraph to build up sympathy for the character through how others treat him/her. Develop tension with questions. Use simile or metaphor to describe the hunger. To keep the reader interested, you should end this paragraph with a snappy suspense sentence – something is about to happen, but what will it be?

Paragraph 3 Use the main character's thoughts and reflections to explore the dilemma they are facing. Use language from a balanced argument to describe these. Don't neglect sense impressions. For variety and interest, it is a good idea to introduce another character in this paragraph – good or bad – whose actions will influence the decision. This character does not need to know the effect they are having, in fact a secret between the main character and reader is what makes for Level 5 writing. Keep your reader guessing by ending this paragraph with the decision made but not shared with the reader.

Paragraph 4 A descriptive time connective will move your character to the point of returning the object. It would be a good idea to use dialogue here.

Paragraph 5 Tie up the loose ends by a couple of sentences about what happened since receiving the reward. Your character should reflect on events and make some observations on what they've learned about human nature or honesty.

Page 36 – Dialogue

A Level 5 answer should contain the following features.

• Variety in the way speech is reported – some use of adverbs, some strong speech verbs and some use of 'said'.
• Dialogue that moves the narrative along.
• Develop characters.
• Make it obvious who is speaking.
• Correct speech punctuation.
• If the sentence ends when the speech ends, the full stop goes inside the closing speech marks.
• If the sentence continues after the speech, a comma goes inside the closing speech marks.
• Question marks and exclamation marks go inside the closing speech marks.
• A new paragraph is started for each new speaker in a passage of dialogue.

Page 37 – Characters' reflections and narrators' comments

A Level 5 answer should contain the following features.

• The character's reflections add to the reader's understanding of their personality.
• The dilemma creates a tension that draws the reader in.
• Show events from more than one point of view.
• The author's comment is designed to influence the reader.

Pages 40–41 – Sentence structure

Nouns and verbs – Suggested answers:

1 Dad stuffed *The Times* into his briefcase and dashed off to work.
2 Mr Patel smiled as I studied the giant size Galaxy bar. "You're still a chocoholic, I see," he teased.
3 Perched on the back seat of the Number 36 was a border collie, looking – it must be said – quite untroubled!
4 Slinging a raincoat over her shoulders, she strode off into the storm.

Adjectives – Suggested answers: Joyous, celebrating, cheering crowd; Sullen, mocking, unmoving crowd; Reassuring, ecstatic, enthusiastic teacher; Stern, glowering, threatening teacher; Gentle, swaying, protective trees; Cruel, dense, unyielding trees; Calm, starry, peaceful night; Lonely, stormy, wild night

Adverbs – Suggested answers: Whispered excitedly – Whispered hoarsely; Ran carelessly – Ran cautiously; Laughed quietly – Laughed as if his sides would split; Knocked desperately – Knocked lightly; Danced joyfully – Danced reluctantly; Slept peacefully – Slept fitfully

Alliteration – Suggested answers:

1 Swans gliding **gracefully** on the lake.
2 He watched **wearily** as the children filed out.
3 Dancing **daintily** from flower to flower, the fairy queen collected nectar.
4 The giant towered **terrifyingly** over us.

Page 42 – Speech punctuation

"What a wonderful day for taking a boat out on the lake," said Ollie joyfully.
"Sure is," Stan answered, "but how about a cool drink beforehand?"
"Great idea," replied Ollie, "except we've only got three pound coins. We've got to buy the girls one as well."
"What can we do?" replied Stan.
"I know," schemed Ollie. "When I ask you what you'd like to drink, you refuse."
"But!"
"No buts," hurried Ollie. "Here are the girls. Now then, a cola for you, a cola for you and a cola for me. Stanley, what will you have?"
"A cola."
"Can't you grasp the situation? We've only got three pounds. When I ask you what you want you must refuse."
"Oh," beamed Stan.
"Sorry girls," grinned Ollie as he regained his composure. "So that's a cola, a cola, a cola and my dear Stanley, what will you have."
"A cola."
"Why do you keep saying a cola?" pleaded Ollie.
"Because you keep asking me," cried Stan.

Page 43 – Apostrophes

a) The boys' books were in a terrible state.   **b)** Sofie's marks were excellent when she studied.   **c)** Philip's shoes were never clean.   **d)** I wouldn't be visiting that shop again.   **e)** Katie didn't finish her work on time.   **f)** Elizabeth's homework got great marks.   **g)** I hadn't got my pocket money yet.   **h)** Tim's class wasn't over until the evening.   **i)** The girls' dance routine shouldn't take more than 5 minutes.   **j)** John's feet didn't touch the ground.

1 Why do you think his teacher changed Rolihlahla's name to Nelson?

_____

1 | 1 mark

2 Do you think Nelson enjoyed his childhood? Use evidence from the text to support your view.

_____

_____

2 | 2 marks

3 Do you think Mandela was brave, foolish or both to go to Johannesburg?

Tick the box you agree with and justify your answer.

Brave ☐   Foolish ☐

_____

_____

3 | 3 marks

4 Nelson Mandela spent a lot of his time making speeches in front of big crowds of people, encouraging them to raise up against the white Government.

How do you think Nelson Mandela felt when he was placed in solitary confinement on Robben Island?

_____

_____

4 | 2 marks

5 a) How might the inmates of the prison have communicated without the guards knowing?

_____

_____

5a | 1 mark

b) What would they be likely to be talking about?

_____

_____

5b | 1 mark

6 Do you think Mandela was a popular leader with white South Africans as well as black? Justify your answer using evidence from the text. Use a separate sheet of paper to write your answer.

6 | 3 marks

Total marks for this topic ☐

23

Poetry

The Listeners

'Is there anybody there?' said the Traveller,
Knocking on the moonlit door;
And his horse in the silence champed the grasses
Of the forest's ferny floor:
And a bird flew up out of the turret,
Above the Traveller's head
And he smote upon the door again a second time;
'Is there anybody there?' he said.
But no one descended to the Traveller;
No head from the leaf-fringed sill
Leaned over and looked into his grey eyes,
Where he stood perplexed and still.
But only a host of phantom listeners
That dwelt in the lone house then
Stood listening in the quiet of the moonlight
To that voice from the world of men:
Stood thronging the faint moonbeams on the dark stair,
That goes down to the empty hall,
Hearkening in an air stirred and shaken
By the lonely Traveller's call.
And he felt in his heart their strangeness,
Their stillness answering his cry,
While his horse moved, cropping the dark turf,
'Neath the starred and leafy sky;
For he suddenly smote on the door, even
Louder, and lifted his head:-
'Tell them I came, and no one answered,
That I kept my word,' he said.
Never the least stir made the listeners,
Though every word he spake
Fell echoing through the shadowiness of the still house
From the one man left awake:
Ay, they heard his foot upon the stirrup,
And the sound of iron on stone,
And how the silence surged softly backward,
When the plunging hoofs were gone.

Walter de la Mare

1 Where do you think the house that the traveller arrived at is? Use evidence from the poem to justify your views.

_____

_____

_____

	1
3 marks	

2 **a)** Who are the listeners?

_____

	2a
1 mark	

b) What has happened to them?

_____

	2b
1 mark	

3 Do you think the traveller happened upon the house by chance or did he go there to meet someone? Use evidence from the text to justify your answer.

_____

_____

	3
2 marks	

4 What do you think *smote* means?

_____

	4
1 mark	

5 Do you think this is a modern or historical poem? What clues are there in the poem that support your view?

_____

_____

	5
2 marks	

6 Where do you think the traveller is going and what information from the poem made you make that decision?

_____

_____

	6
2 marks	

7 Did you enjoy this poem? Use evidence from the poem to back up your view.

_____

_____

_____

	7
3 marks	

Total marks for this topic

Tale of courage

It is important to be able to write in the first person (as if you are the main character) because some story titles require this. To write successfully in the first person, you must remember you can only develop other characters through your interpretation of their behaviour. It is still a story so you can alter who 'you' are to suit the story.

Write a tale of courage with yourself as the main character. Plan your story on this page, then write your 'tale of courage' in full on a separate sheet of paper.

Here is a story mapped onto a paragraph plan.	Use this space to plan your narrative.
Paragraph 1 Open with the setting, introduce yourself by what you think and do. Hint at your fear.	_____ _____ _____
Paragraph 2 The fear is exposed and you suffer as a result.	_____ _____ _____
Paragraph 3 Some time later, you are face to face with the fear again. Someone needs your help and you are going to have to overcome your fear to help them.	_____ _____ _____
Paragraph 4 Putting others before yourself, you confront and overcome your fear.	_____ _____ _____
Paragraph 5 The unhappiness is resolved and you reflect on the events.	_____ _____ _____

Independent writing

Plan and write another first person story on one of these themes.

★ Losing something important you had been trusted with.
★ Caught telling a lie.
★ Finding a stray dog you really want to keep.

A cautionary tale

To achieve Level 5, it is necessary to vary the straightforward timeline of events. One technique for doing this is using a flashback.

Write a cliff rescue story following a flashback structure. First, plan your story on this page, then write your 'cautionary tale' in full on a separate sheet of paper.

Here is a story mapped onto a paragraph plan.	Use this space to plan your narrative.
Paragraph 1 The children are in trouble.	_____ _____ _____
Paragraph 2 FLASHBACK: The parents' warning to the children earlier that day.	_____ _____ _____
Paragraph 3 The danger/trouble worsens.	_____ _____ _____
Paragraph 4 The rescue.	_____ _____ _____
Paragraph 5 Parents find out and their responses. Characters' reflection on the experience and lesson learned.	_____ _____ _____

Independent writing

Plan and write your own adventure or suspense story using one of these titles.

★ A Foolish Boast
★ Noises in the Night
★ Just Another Shopping Trip
★ The Unusual Gift

Remember, start your story at an action point and use a flashback to fill in the events up to this point.

A historical tale

To achieve Level 5, you must show understanding of the features and style of a traditional tale. Good-versus-evil characterisation is the most important feature. You must conclude with a resolution (tying up) of the story followed by reflections, showing the impact of the events on some key characters, and end with a moral and/or 'happily ever after'.

Write a traditional story with the youngest child of three as the hero and a seemingly insignificant gift saving him/her. First, plan your story on this page, then write your 'tale of long ago' in full on a separate sheet of paper.

Here is a story mapped onto a paragraph plan.	Use this space to plan your narrative.
Paragraph 1 Traditional tale opening. Introduce the hero (good), the youngest of three brothers/sisters (cowardly, selfish etc.).	_____ _____ _____
Paragraph 2 Characters required to do a good deed; first two fail/refuse.	_____ _____ _____
Paragraph 3 Youngest needs to do his/her own deed; involves a sacrifice; makes the right choice and is rewarded with a gift or advice.	_____ _____ _____
Paragraph 4 Some time later the hero faces an improbable challenge. The 'gift' comes to his aid and he succeeds.	_____ _____ _____
Paragraph 5 The hero's improved circumstances explained and 'bad' characters reform or are punished. The moral and 'happily ever after'.	_____ _____ _____

Independent writing

Plan and write your own traditional tale around one of these themes.

★ Three wishes – the first two are wasted.

★ A young man sets out to make his fortune.

★ Good deeds leading to the release of someone trapped in an ugly/unpleasant form.

Persuasion 1

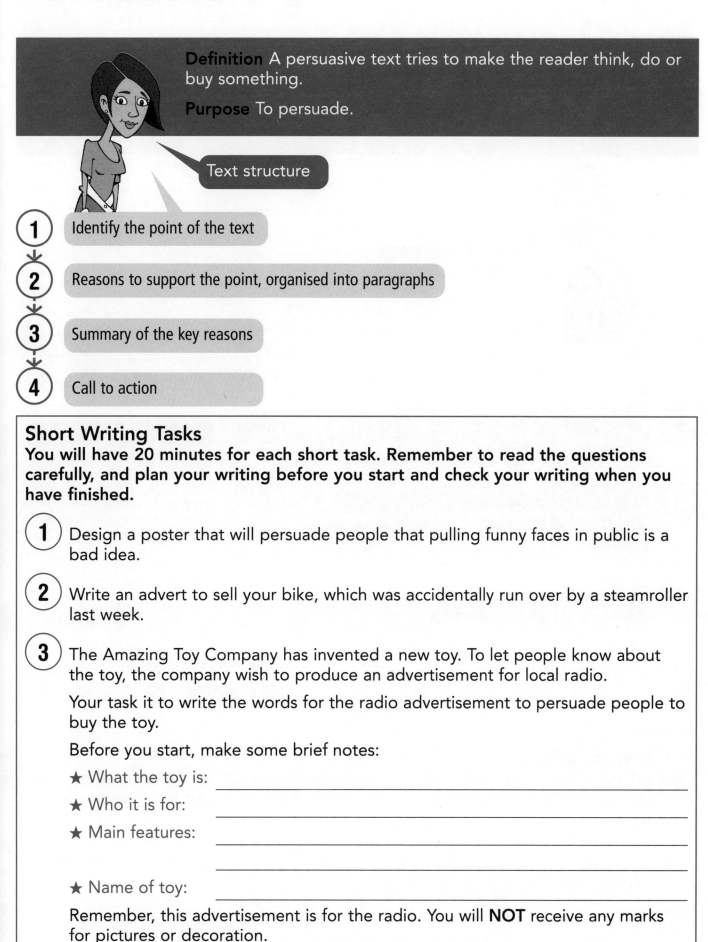

Definition A persuasive text tries to make the reader think, do or buy something.

Purpose To persuade.

Text structure

1 Identify the point of the text

2 Reasons to support the point, organised into paragraphs

3 Summary of the key reasons

4 Call to action

Short Writing Tasks

You will have 20 minutes for each short task. Remember to read the questions carefully, and plan your writing before you start and check your writing when you have finished.

1 Design a poster that will persuade people that pulling funny faces in public is a bad idea.

2 Write an advert to sell your bike, which was accidentally run over by a steamroller last week.

3 The Amazing Toy Company has invented a new toy. To let people know about the toy, the company wish to produce an advertisement for local radio.

Your task it to write the words for the radio advertisement to persuade people to buy the toy.

Before you start, make some brief notes:

★ What the toy is: _____

★ Who it is for: _____

★ Main features: _____

_____

★ Name of toy: _____

Remember, this advertisement is for the radio. You will **NOT** receive any marks for pictures or decoration.

Have a go at turning your plan into a piece of text on a separate piece of paper.

Explanation

Definition An explanation tells the reader how or why something works or happens. It can be about natural things, e.g. how lakes are formed, or about mechanical things, e.g. how a telephone works.

Purpose To explain.

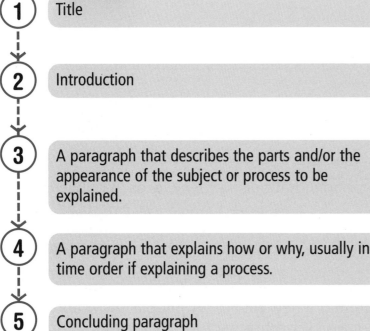

Text structure

1 Title — Tells the reader what the explanation is about. Often contains *how* or *why*.

2 Introduction — Definition of the subject of the explanation.

3 A paragraph that describes the parts and/or the appearance of the subject or process to be explained.

4 A paragraph that explains how or why, usually in time order if explaining a process.

5 Concluding paragraph — Could include where the subject can be found or what it is used for.

Short Writing Tasks

You will have 20 minutes for each short task. Remember to read the question carefully, plan your writing before you start and check your writing when you have finished.

1 Write an explanation leaflet that tells the reader how to stop little brothers and sisters from playing with their things.

2 Write a note to your teacher explaining why you have failed to hand in any of your homework on time since the beginning of the year.

Non-chronological report

Definition Non-chronological reports give a reader information about something or somewhere. They are usually about a group of things, e.g. dinosaurs, not one thing in particular, e.g. Dilly the dinosaur. Facts about the subject are organised into paragraphs.

Purpose To give information.

Text structure

1 Title — Usually the subject of the report.

2 Introduction — Definition of the subject of the report.

3 Series of paragraphs about various aspects of the subject

4 Rounding off statement — Could include where the subject can be found or what it is used for.

Short Writing Tasks
You will have 20 minutes for each short task. Remember to read the question carefully, plan your writing before you start and check your writing when you have finished.

1 Write a short *Guide Book for Parents* for when parents want to visit your classroom.

2 Write a postcard to your best friend telling them all about the luxury 5-star hotel you are staying in on holiday.

3 Imagine a creature called a Tongo Lizard.

It is an endangered creature, which means that very few remain and it may become extinct. An information book about endangered creatures is being prepared.

Your task is to write the page about the Tongo Lizard. You can make up the information using your imagination.

Use a separate sheet of paper to plan your writing.
Have a go at turning your plan into a piece of text.

Balanced argument 1

Definition A balanced argument gives the reader information about an issue from different points of view, then leaves the reader to make up their mind about how they feel about the issue.

Purpose To present a balanced argument.

Text structure

1	Title	**Often in the form of a question.**
2	Identify the issue	
3	Points to support the issue	
4	Points against the issue	
5	Summary	

Short Writing Tasks

You will have 20 minutes for each short task. Remember to read the question carefully, plan your writing before you start and check your writing when you have fininshed.

1 List in table form the arguments for and against children using mobile phones in school.

2 List in table form the arguments for and against school canteens selling 'fast food' to children at lunchtime.

Recount

Definition A recount tells the reader about something that has happened in the past. It might have happened to the writer or to someone else.

Purpose To retell an event or events.

Text plan: Newspaper report on street muggings

1 Orientation – this is the information that helps the reader understand the recount (who, where, when, why).

Introduce the subject of mugging and the person to be interviewed about their experience.

2 Recount events in chronological order (as they happened), making sure the event is broken down clearly.

Describe the interviewee in more detail. Why was he/she walking home late? Describe the events in a blow-by-blow way.

3 Give some personal comment or reflection about the event.

Reflections about what else he/she could have done to keep safe.

4 Sum up by returning to some of the main points as an ending comment. Some evaluation may be appropriate.

Evaluate the impact on his/her life. Suggest action that might be taken.

Complete this recount about muggings in the form of a newspaper report, taking care to write chronologically and to use relevant detail and description. Make sure you use reported speech as part of your piece. Use the paragraph prompts to help you shape your answer.

Independent writing

Plan and write your own recount using one of these ideas. Remember to use the structure above.

★ The diary entry of Henry VIII after he had decided to execute Anne Boleyn.

★ A letter to an aunt from someone who met the Queen at a Jubilee celebration.

★ A biography of your life so far.

Persuasion 2

> **Definition** A persuasive text tries to make the reader think, do or buy something.
>
> **Purpose** To persuade.

In this scene, Joe is desperately trying to persuade his parents that he should be allowed to stay up late to watch TV.

Your task is to continue the playscript set out below.

Scene 1

Joe: (*pleading*) Dad, can I stay up to watch something special on the TV tonight?

Dad: I don't know, it depends on what it is …

Mum: (*coming into the room*) … And what time it finishes.

Your task is to continue this scene until a decision is reached. Remember that Joe is trying to persuade his parents.

Use a separate sheet of paper to plan your writing.

Independent writing

Have a go at turning your plan into a piece of text. Why not try planning and writing these titles too.

★ Should school uniform be banned

★ Children should not be allowed to eat fast food

★ Pocket money should be compulsory and at least £20 a week

Balanced argument 2

Definition A balanced argument gives the reader information about an issue from different points of view, then leaves the reader to make up their mind about how they feel about the issue.

Purpose To present a balanced argument.

Your class was asked to try out a new kind of school bag which was designed to carry books and equipment in school – the *Pack-it-in-Bag*.

You all tried the new bag for a month and although it worked well in some ways, it wasn't a complete success.

Your task is to write a report for the company to tell them how well the *Pack-it-in-Bag* works, and to give them some information that might help them to improve it.

The company have asked you to report on:
★ whether the bag is made from suitable materials;
★ whether all the things you need for school can fit inside the bag;
★ whether the bag is strong enough to carry the things you need;
★ things that could be improved.

Use a separate sheet of paper to plan your writing.

Independent writing

Have a go at turning your plan into a piece of text. Why not have a go writing discussion texts about the following topics.

★ School uniform is a good thing
★ Television is not good for children
★ School dinners are more healthy than packed lunches

Dialogue

★ Use dialogue to develop your character in a way that is relevant to the plot.

★ Use it instead of action to move the story along (but take care not to overuse it). Dialogue is not simply speech, it is also how characters speak.

★ Vary the way you report speech. You must use adverbs and strong verbs but too many sounds contrived; a simple 'he said' could be the best choice.

★ Always make it obvious who is speaking. You must use correct speech punctuation.

Choose one scene from the choices below and use dialogue to develop it into paragraphs using the ideas above.

(1) An unexpected caller talking through a letterbox to a child who has been told not to open the door to anyone.

(2) Two children find an unusual package.

(3) A woman in a shop has her purse stolen. A teenage girl chases after the suspect.

_____

_____

_____

_____

_____

_____

_____

_____

_____

_____

_____

_____

_____

_____

_____

_____

_____

_____

_____

Characters' reflections and narrators' comments

★ Develop depth in characters by showing inner conflicts through their reflections; these thoughts should be connected with *but* or *on the other hand*.

★ Characters can reflect on changes within themselves – a good way to end a story.

★ Contrast two characters, or develop their relationship, by showing the reflections of both on the same event.

★ Narrator's comments are a way of including another viewpoint, summarising events or influencing the reader's view of characters.

Choose one scene from the choices below and use reflections and the narrator's comments to develop it into paragraphs using the ideas above.

(1) A girl is given a present by her grandmother. She is sure it will be an unwanted knitted cardigan. Mother is watching, scared that her daughter will be rude about the gift.

(2) Tom found a fox cub and tried to keep it but eventually realised that it was unkind to make it into a pet. He is in the kitchen with his dad, having just returned from the animal refuge where they left the cub. It is the end of the story.

(3) At a sleepover, one child hears a strange noise and wants to go to investigate. The other child is tired and doesn't want to get out of bed.

_____
_____
_____
_____
_____
_____
_____
_____
_____
_____
_____
_____
_____
_____
_____

Adventure stories

A brother and sister went on a day out with their family. Tom really enjoyed the outing, but Sara did not.

That was a great day out! I really hope we can go there again.

Well, what an awful day. Apart from lunch, I can't think of one single thing I enjoyed.

When they returned home, Tom and Sara wrote about the day in their diaries.

Your task is to write Tom and Sara's diary entries.

Use your imagination to decide what Tom and Sara would write in their diaries.

Use the space below to plan your writing.

_____

_____

_____

_____

_____

_____

Have a go at turning your plan into a piece of text on a separate piece of paper.

Independent writing

Plan and write your own adventure story using one of these titles.

★ Escape from Shark Island
★ The Return of the Masked Avenger
★ The Golden Statue and the City of Lost Souls
★ Crisis at 30,000 ft!
★ Stranded in the Sahara . . .
★ Journey to the Bottom of the Sea
★ Rescued!

Modern story

Here is a storyboard about a boy buying a new game.

1

2

3

4

Your task is to write a story based on the events in the storyboard above.

You must decide how the story ends.

Use the space below to plan your writing.

_____

_____

_____

_____

_____

_____

_____

Have a go at turning your plan into a piece of text on a separate piece of paper.

Independent writing

Plan and write your own adventure story using one of these titles.

★ The BMX and Scooter Grand Prix   ★ How I Got to Be on TV!

★ Bad Day at St. Bart's Juniors   ★ The Lost Diary

★ My Dad Was an Alien!   ★ The Toy that Came to Life

★ The Strangest Birthday Present

Sentence structure

Nouns and verbs

Accurate nouns and powerful verbs can be more effective than adjectives and adverbs in some cases.

Rewrite these sentences improving the verbs and nouns.

1 Dad put the newspapers into his bag and went off to work.

_____

_____

2 The shopkeeper smiled as I looked at the biggest chocolate bar. 'You're still a chocoholic, I see,' he said.

_____

_____

3 Sitting on the back seat of the bus was a large, black and white dog, looking – it must be said – quite happy!

_____

_____

4 Putting on her coat, she went out into the cold and windy evening.

_____

_____

Adjectives

Adjectives are used to add something NEW to a noun e.g. _a severe look_ is quite different from _an encouraging look_.

Add an adjective to the words in the first column to create a happy mood and in the second column to create a menacing mood.

	crowd		crowd
	teacher		teacher
	trees		trees
	night		night

Adverbs

Adverbs refine the meaning of a verb. Sometimes a phrase acts as an adverb e.g. sobbed *as if her heart would break*. Never use adverbs that mean the same as the verb, e.g. raced quickly.

Use an adverb to say something different about the verb in each column.

Whispered	Whispered
Ran	Ran
Laughed	Laughed
Knocked	Knocked
Danced	Danced
Slept	Slept

Choose words for their sound as well as their meaning. Words with the same initial sound work well together.

Alliteration
Add an alliterative adverb to these sentences.

1. Swans gliding _____ on the lake.

2. He watched _____ as the children filed out.

3. Dancing _____ from flower to flower, the fairy queen

   collected nectar.

4. The giant towered _____ over us.

Speech punctuation

Use what you have learned about direct speech punctuation to punctuate this conversation. It is based on a script from a Laurel and Hardy film called *Men O' War* made in 1929. Stan and Ollie are two sailors on shore leave. They have just met two girls in the park and they're keen to make a good impression ...

Re-write the speech, putting in the missing speech marks to bring the situation to life!

What a wonderful day for taking a boat out on the lake, said Ollie joyfully.

Sure is, Stan answered but how about a cool drink beforehand.

Great idea, replied Ollie except we've only got three pound coins. We've got to buy the girls one as well.

What can we do? replied Stan.

I know, schemed Ollie. When I ask you what you'd like to drink, you refuse.

But!

No buts, hurried Ollie. Here are the girls. Now then, a cola for you, a cola for you and a cola for me. Stanley, what will you have?

A cola.

Can't you grasp the situation? We've only got three pound coins. When I ask you what you want you must refuse.

Oh, beamed Stan.

Sorry girls, grinned Ollie as he regained his composure. So that's a cola, a cola, a cola and my dear Stanley, what will you have?

A cola.

Why do you keep saying a cola? pleaded Ollie.

Because you keep asking me, cried Stan.

Apostrophes

Apostrophes to show possession
We use apostrophes to show that something belongs to somebody (possession). *The cat's pyjamas!*
Remember – if the noun is plural the apostrophe moves. *The cats' pyjamas!*
Apostrophes to show omission
We also use apostrophes to show that a letter has been missed out (omission). *Did not* becomes *didn't.*

Re-write these sentences adding in the apostrophes where they are needed. Watch out for the last three!

a) The boys books were in a terrible state. (plural)

_____

b) Sofies marks were excellent when she studied.

_____

c) Philips shoes were never clean.

_____

d) I would not be visiting that shop again.

_____

e) Katie did not finish her work on time.

_____

f) Elizabeths homework got great marks.

_____

g) I had not got my pocket money yet.

_____

h) Tims class was not over until the evening.

_____

i) The girls dance routine should not take more than five minutes. (plural)

_____

j) Johns feet did not touch the ground.

_____

Thank you for buying this book!

Rising Stars publish a fantastic range of books and software.
You can find out more on our website at www.risingstars-uk.com.

We'd love to hear what you think about this book. Email your
comment to us at joannemitchell@risingstars-uk.com.